EASY STRING MU
Series Editor: Sheila M. N

WAGGON WHEELS
for Violin and Piano

by
Katherine and Hugh Colledge

Piano part

BOOSEY&HAWKES

London · New York · Berlin · Sydney

Composers' Note

In this collection of pieces for beginners, we have adopted a "slowly but surely" approach. By gradually introducing new ideas and giving several examples to illustrate each point, the student has the opportunity to consolidate newly-acquired skills and build a firm foundation for future learning.

This book, which is a sequel to **Stepping Stones**, (Boosey & Hawkes, *7948*), covers 2nd, 3rd and 4th fingers (in 1-23-4 pattern) and slurred bowing.

In order to keep the music as simple as possible, expression marks and so on have been omitted until *Hills and dales* onwards but, of course, teachers and pupils may always add their own.

With one exception, the piano introductions are optional. Except in *With an upbeat*, the introductory 'rest' bars have not been included in the violin part, although the length of the introduction is indicated at the top of each piece. For this reason, in Nos.13, 20 and 26 the *D.C. al Fine* in the violin part corresponds with the *D.S. al Fine* in the piano part.

Katherine and Hugh Colledge
London, England, 1988

Anmerkung der Komponisten

In dieser Sammlung von Stücken für den Anfänger sind wir nach dem Motto "langsam aber sicher" vorgegangen. Neue Ideen werden allmählich eingeführt und durch entsprechende Beispiele veranschaulicht. Dadurch hat der Schüler die Möglichkeit, die neu erworbenen Fähigkeiten zu festigen und eine feste Grundlage für das weitere Lernen aufzubauen.

Dieser Band, der eine Fortsetzung von **Stepping Stones** (Boosey & Hawkes, *7948*) ist, behandelt den 2., 3. und 4. Finger (nach dem Schema 1–23–4) und die verschleifende Bogenführung.

Um die Musik so einfach wie möglich zu halten, wurden bis *Hills and dales* die Ausdruckszeichen und dergl. weggelassen. Diese können vom Lehrer oder Schüler jedoch jederzeit eingefügt werden.

Mit einer Ausnahme sind die Klaviereinleitungen ad lib. Außer in *With an upbeat* wurden die einleitenden "Pausen"-Takte in der Violinstimme weggelassen, aber die Länge der Einleitung ist zu Beginn eines jeden Stückes vermerkt. Aus diesem Grund entspricht das *D.C. al Fine* in der Violinstimme in den Nummern 13, 30 und 26 dem *D.S. al Fine* in der Klavierstimme.

Katherine und Hugh Colledge
London, England, 1988

Note des Compositeurs

Dans ce recueil de morceaux pour débutants, nous avons adoptés la manière "lentement mais sûrement". En introduisant graduellement des nouvelles idées et en donnant plusieurs exemples pour illustrer chaque point, l'étudiant a l'opportunité de consolider sa technique nouvellement acquise et de bâtir une base solide pour ses études futures.

Ce livre, qui est la suite de **Stepping Stones**, (Boosey & Hawkes, *7948*), couvre les second, 3ème et 4ème doigts (sur le modèle 1-23-4), et le lié de l'archet.

De façon à garder la musique aussi simple que possible, nous n'avons pas marqué les nuances jusqu'à *Hills and dales*, mais naturellement les professeurs et les élèves peuvent toujours ajouter les leurs.

A une exception près, les introductions du piano sont facultatives. Sauf *With an upbeat*, les mesures de "silence" préliminaires ne sont pas indiquées sur la partition de violon, bien que la longueur de l'introduction soit signalée en haut de chaque morceau. Pour cette raison, dans les numéros 13, 20 et 26 le *D.C. al Fine* sur la partition de violon correspond au *D.S. al Fine* sur la partition de piano.

Katherine et Hugh Colledge
Londres, Angleterre, 1988

作曲者注釈

　この初心者のための曲集では、"ゆっくりとしかし正確に"という方針を採用しています。新しいアイデアを段階的に紹介したり、各々のポイントを説明するためのいくつかの例を示すことによって、生徒達は新しく得た技術を強化することができ、将来の勉強のためにしっかりとした基礎を築くことができるのです。

　この"ステッピング・ストーン"(ブージー・アンド・ホークス、7948)に続く本では、二の指、三の指と四の指(1-23-4のパターン)とスラー・ボーイングを紹介しています。

　楽譜を極力簡単にするために、表示記号などはヒルス・アンド・デイルスの前まで省略してありますが、当然先生や生徒達は自分達で書き入れてもかまいません。

　一つの例外、ウィズ・アン・アップビートを除けば、ピアノの序奏はオプションで、序奏の休みの小節はヴァイオリン・パートには入っていませんが、しかし序奏の長さは各曲の最初に示してあります。このため、13番、20番と26番のヴァイオリン・パートのD.C. al Fineとピアノ・パートのD.S. al Fineと一致するのです。

キャサリン・アンド・ホー・カレッジ
ロンドン、イングランド、1988.　。

WAGGON WHEELS

KATHERINE and HUGH COLLEDGE

1. In a garden

B. & H. 20847

2. Summer breeze

3

4

3. Goldfish bowl

con Ped.

4. Penny-farthing

5. Butterflies

6. Westminster Abbey

7. Dinosaurs

8. Paddle steamer

10

9. Waterfall

con Ped.

10. Knickerbocker glory

pizz.

11. Hills and dales

Not too fast

12. Upstairs, downstairs

13. Daydreaming

D.S. al Fine

14. Bell-ringers

16

15. Polka dots

16. Nightingale

17. Chinese lanterns

18. Fiddlesticks

19. Windscreen wipers

20. Bow ties!

19. Windscreen wipers

20. Bow ties!

Ped.

D.S. al Fine

21. Ice dancers

22. Full moon

23. Waggon wheels

23

24

21. Ice dancers

24. With an upbeat

25. On the wing

26. Lollipop man

D.S. al Fine

Printed by
Halstan & Co. Ltd., Amersham, Bucks., England